In Soul Motion

Journal Prompts to Set Your Soul In Motion

Cheryl Carrigan

In Soul Motion

Journal Prompts to Set Your Soul in Motion

By Cheryl Carrigan

Published by

Transcendent Publishing
P.O. Box 66202
St. Pete Beach, FL 33736
www.transcendentpublishing.com

ISBN-10: 0-9987576-0-8
ISBN-13: 978-0-9987576-0-5

Printed in the United States of America.

Dedication

This journal is dedicated to one of the strongest, dearest women I have ever met. She, without any hesitation, could conquer any situation with amazing ease and grace. She has the internal soul strength that comes from a heritage of strong women, with an unwavering dedication to her family like no other. If I could create a family avatar it would look very similar to Betty Boop ... a small dark-haired woman with ruby red lips that can make the world a better place just by being around her—that avatar would be made in the form of my mom ... Darleen Carrigan.

My mom has never had a really, really bad day; even when things are what most people would find as hard, she always has some silver lining or good she can pull out of nowhere. My own inspiration to inspire others to live a happy life comes from her. Even in my darkest moment, mom would say, "Go ahead and cry, I am listening," and when I got it all out she found the words to patch my heart together so I could make it through the day.

Mom taught me that Mondays are the only day to start my diets ... only after indulging in a delicious hot fudge Sunday over the weekend!

Sometimes I save her voice messages on my phone just so I can replay them when I need to feel her energy—it always makes me smile.

My mom calls me every day and inspires me to be my best *me*, and so as a gift to honor her ...

My wish for you is that you will open these pages and feel the love of my mom shine through. It will make you smile.

Thanks mom ... I love you with all of my heart!

Love,
Cheryl

In Soul Motion

When Your Soul Is In Motion...
Your Life Is In Motion!

Ignite your fire today!

Your imagination is on fire today. Use this energy to paint the picture of what your ideal lifestyle would be ... come on, I dare you to make your life amazing ... be amazing, live amazingly! Why not?
Write what you really, truly want your life to be like.

playing concerts, singing, playing instruments - i have animals & the best partner, soul mate the Divine has ever sent me. i love my children & animals. i always have more than enough. The Divine provider my needs + i have full faith + trust in the Divine. i clearly see hear feel + follow Divine Guidance + live my life according to Divine will. i help many people every day + still have time for me + all that is important to me.

_____

Enjoy the climb!

Today is a day to take one step at a time. No rushing ... just be present in the moment and listen for guidance for what your next step should be. What is your next step?

Breathe ...
Repeat!

Today, let's take some
time for you ... breathe in
... breath out!
When we take time for
ourselves we tell the
soul how truly loved it is.
Write a note here to
your soul.

_____

_____

_____

_____

_____

_____

_____

_____

_____

_____

Spread Kindness Today!

Spread some kindness today ... to both yourself and others. When was the last time you wrote a note to yourself reflecting on your life, all that you have accomplished/ overcome /walked through? Take a moment and write a note of kindness to you!

_____

_____

_____

_____

_____

_____

_____

_____

_____

_____

_____

_____

_____

Go with the flow today...

Letting go and just allowing is so very, very freeing ...
I dare you ... let go of control, just be free and in the flow!
What do you hold on to and try to control?
What would happen if you let it go?

_____

_____

_____

_____

_____

_____

_____

_____

You are Perfect

Today's message is simple ...
There is no one to compare
yourself to, or look up to,
other than yourself.
You are perfect just
the way you are.
Write down everything you
love about you!

_____

_____

_____

_____

_____

_____

_____

_____

_____

_____

_____

_____

_____

_____

_____

_____

_____

_____

_____

_____

_____

_____

_____

_____

Cheers to our Friendships

Sometimes it is the simple moments shared with a friend that change the direction of our life. Call a friend and thank them for being in your life. Make a list of all the important friendships in your life and what makes them so special.

_____
_____
_____
_____
_____
_____
_____
_____
_____
_____
_____
_____
_____
_____
_____

Take a Drive

Today is the perfect day
for a drive.
Fill up the tank and see
where the road takes you ...
look for Angels along the
way, don't forget to count
your blessings!
Make a list of some fun
destinations you can drive
to, then turn the key
and let's go!

Hugs Heal

Today is a hugging kind of day.
Reach out and hug a friend,
call and share a hug over the
phone, or simply send a text ...
send hugs out to the world.
What makes a hug so special?

_____
_____
_____

_____
_____
_____
_____
_____

It's a Great Day!

Today, let's look for the many special signs that remind you that it is indeed a great day to be alive! Make a list of everything that makes this day great!

_____
_____
_____
_____
_____
_____
_____
_____
_____

Doodles & Dreams...

...and More!

_____

_____

_____

_____

_____

_____

_____

Light up the World!

Today, let's open up and show our true selves to the world. You are perfect just as you are ... don't hide a thing today, go be the amazing person that you are! What keeps you from showing up as your true self?

_____

_____

_____

_____

_____

_____

_____

_____

_____

_____

Forgiveness Frees YOU!

The biggest gift you can give yourself is forgiveness!
Hold your hand on your heart and say,
"I forgive you."
Jot down everything you hold yourself accountable for, and when you are done, hold your hand over your heart and release it!
Free yourself today.

_____

_____

_____

_____

_____

_____

_____

_____

_____

_____

_____

_____

_____

_____

_____

_____

Let's SOAR!

Today, let's spread our wings and soar like eagles. Fly high enough to see the bigger picture, circle around to get all the details, then swoop in and make your life happen! What are you going to make happen today?

_____

_____

_____

_____

_____

_____

_____

_____

Find Your Tribe

Today, let's gather your tribe ...
your "go-to" people.
The ones who make you
shine brighter than you
thought possible.
Surround yourself with your
tribe and watch the
magic happen!
Dear Angels, please bring me ...

_____
_____
_____
_____
_____
_____
_____

_____
_____
_____
_____
_____
_____
_____
_____
_____
_____
_____
_____
_____
_____
_____
_____

_____

_____

_____

_____

_____

_____

_____

_____

Follow the Rainbow!

Rainbows and sunshine appear after the storms.
Take out your umbrella and dance in the rain ... then look
for the rainbows. Have you ever just went outside and
danced in the rain? Dancing in the rain is freeing and will
remind you that this too shall pass, just like the storm.
What is on the other side of the rainbow for you?

_____

_____

_____

_____

_____

_____

_____

_____

Money, Money, Money!

Visualize money falling from the sky, visualize it piling on a chair, falling out of the cupboards ... visualize it absolutely everywhere! Where are all the places you visualize it?

_____

_____

_____

_____

_____

_____

_____

_____

_____

_____

_____

_____

_____

_____

_____

_____

_____

_____

_____

_____

_____

_____

_____

_____

_____

_____

_____

_____

_____

_____

Let Your Inner Child Play!

Let's do something creative ... oftentimes we shut down our creative side for fear we won't do "it" well enough. Today, let's make a basket full of fun things that open up our creative side ... I dare you! What will you put in your creative basket?

_____

_____

_____

_____

_____

_____
_____
_____
_____
_____
_____
_____
_____

New Beginnings

Have you wanted to start something that you keep putting off? Today, start one new thing that makes you feel good ... take a morning walk, smile more, say hello to strangers when passing by, worry less.

It is amazing how changing one simple thing changes your attitude, which changes your happiness.

What new beginning will you start today?

_____
_____
_____
_____

_____

_____

_____

_____

_____

_____

_____

_____

_____

_____

Intention

Today, I want you to think about a word ... intention.
How often in your day are you focused?
How often does your mind wander?
Today, let's be purposeful with our intentions, so we can stay true to our greatest desires!
You deserve it!
What are your intentions for today?

_____

_____

_____

_____

_____

_____

_____

_____

_____

_____

_____

_____

_____

_____

_____

_____

_____

_____

Stand Up for Yourself!

Today, I am going to challenge you to stand up for yourself,
to speak your truth.
Many times we keep quite because we are afraid if we
say what we are thinking, people will judge us.
Who cares what people think?
Most people are too self-centered to care.
So today, I give you permission to speak your truth.
Whatever it is you want heard, say and watch the magic happen.
What truth do you want heard today?

_____

_____

_____

_____

_____

_____

_____

_____
_____
_____
_____

Release!

Today, let's take a step back
and let go of everything that
we no longer need to carry
with us on this journey
called life.
Let go of your worries and
cares, let go of the things in
our homes that you no
longer need.
If you're full of worries and
cares, you have no room for
happiness and bliss ...
see how wonderful you feel
when you let go.
Make a list of what and
where in your life
you will release.

_____
_____
_____
_____
_____
_____
_____
_____
_____
_____
_____

_____
_____
_____
_____

You are Very Special

I want you to know how truly
special you are to this earth.
There is no one on this earth
that is like you ... no one.
You are an original,
a one of a kind.
Today, I want you to know not
only how special you are,
but how loved you are.
So, you very special, loved
human, go have a fantastic day!
What are you going to do to
make yourself feel special
today?

Doodles & Dreams...

...and More!

Soften Your Words!

Today, let's watch our words ... only use words from the uplifting zone. Use words for good; try touching people's hearts and souls with words that lift them up! When you touch people's hearts and souls, it comes back to you two fold. Make a list of ways you can soften your words.

_____

_____

_____

_____

_____

_____

_____

_____

_____

_____

_____

_____

_____

_____

_____

_____

_____

_____

_____

_____

_____

_____

_____

_____

_____

_____

_____

_____

_____

_____

_____

_____

_____

_____

_____

_____

_____

_____

Live Big!

Think BIG and dream
even BIGGER ... then
go make those BIG
dreams come true.
Come on, don't let
anyone, or anything,
keep you from
living your dreams.
Make a list of your
BIGGEST dreams...

Breathe

Today, let's keep it simple.
Breathe ... exhale ... repeat.
Do this over and over while
holding your hands on your heart.
What do you feel when you hold
your hands on your heart?
Say, "I AM" and write what
comes to you ...

_____
_____
_____
_____
_____
_____
_____
_____
_____

Let's Dance!

Hey DJ!
Turn the music up and let's dance to some happy music.
Music makes us feel happy.
When you feel happy, you have a big smile on your
face and in your heart!
So come on, turn up the happy dance!
Make a list of songs that make you happy…

_____
_____
_____
_____
_____
_____
_____
_____

Gratitude

Today, look around
and truly appreciate
all the beauty that
surrounds you.
I mean, really look
around and take an
inventory of all the
cool, amazing things
in your life.
Say thanks and feel
the gratitude fill
your heart.
Today, let's take an
inventory of all the
good cool stuff in
your life ...
then hold your hand
on your heart and feel
gratitude!

_____

_____

_____

_____

_____

_____

_____

_____

_____

Show Me Your Friends!

Energies are contagious...
Today, surround yourself
with people who inspire
you with their way of life.
When you surround
yourself with awesome
people, it's amazing how
awesome YOU become!
Who are the people who
inspire you and why?

_____

_____

_____

_____

_____

_____

_____

_____

_____

_____

_____

_____

_____

_____
_____
_____
_____
_____
_____
_____
_____
_____
_____
_____

Heart Connection!

Today, let's find ourselves a peaceful spot to sit and connect to our heart and soul.
Hold your hand over your heart and ask any question you want ... then wait, be still and listen.
What did you hear/feel/sense?

_____

_____

_____

_____

_____

_____

_____

_____

_____

Let's start a new habit today.

What if we spend 15 minutes today, and every day,
taking care of ourselves?
Putting ourselves on our calendars, making us a priority,
living our life purpose and being true to our heart and soul.
How are you going to take care of your self today?
Tomorrow ... all year?

_____

_____

_____

_____

_____

_____

_____

_____

_____

Doodles and Dreams..

...and More!

Only What YOU Think Matters!

Just for today ... stop wasting
your time worrying about
what others think.
Ask yourself, "What do I think?"
Focus on YOUR thoughts,
YOUR desires.
YOU matter to this world.
Write what YOU think of
yourself or a situation, then hold
true to your thoughts.

True Power!

Today, let's stand in your true power. Place your hands on your heart, go inside yourself ... and ask for the guidance, the strength and the courage to resolve any situation that lies in front of you.
You can do it ...
I promise you can!

_____
_____
_____
_____
_____
_____
_____
_____
_____

_____
_____
_____
_____
_____
_____
_____
_____
_____
_____
_____
_____
_____
_____
_____
_____

_____

_____

_____

_____

_____

_____

_____

_____

_____

Laughter Heals!

Today, let's be grateful for the people who make us laugh! Laughter is healing to the heart and soul. Today, make a point to spread laughter, where ever we go, whatever we do, find something to laugh about. Who are the people in your life that make you laugh?

_____

_____

_____

_____

_____

_____

_____

_____

_____

_____
_____
_____
_____
_____
_____
_____
_____
_____
_____
_____
_____

Thankful, Grateful and Kind.

Let today be a day we are thankful for all we have, grateful of what is coming and kind to everyone ... especially ourselves. Today, list what you are thankful, grateful and kind to.

Nourish Your Heart!

Today, let's set aside a few minutes to do something that your heart finds nourishing … like mediation, taking a walk, or having a cup of tea. Today, take time for you! What are you going to do for your heart today?

Let GO!

Today, let's practice letting go. Let go of the need to control, it is just an illusion anyway.
As you surrender the desire to control, you slip into a relaxed energy that will rapidly attract any and all of your wildest desires.
Enjoy!

_____
_____
_____
_____
_____
_____
_____
_____
_____
_____
_____
_____
_____
_____

Realize Your Potential!

You are an amazing, powerful soul that has the potential to make an amazing and powerful impact on this earth … don't ever forget this. This earth needs souls like you.

_____
_____
_____
_____
_____
_____
_____
_____

_____

_____

_____

_____

_____

_____

_____

_____

No Bad Days!

Life is so short and every day is a special gift, so let's live
with the thought that there are no bad days! Some days
are amazing. others are good, and others, well they may
not be the best, but there are still no BAD days!

_____

_____

_____

_____

_____

_____

_____

_____

_____

Have a Great Day!

Wow, today is such an amazingly perfect day! Pack yourself a picnic lunch, then go out and discover just how perfect today can be. When we do things out of the routine, it makes it special, and who doesn't want to feel special ...
Have a Great Day!

_____

_____

_____

_____

_____

_____

_____

_____

_____

_____

Your Pathway
is Lit

Are you waiting for the
pathway in front of you to
light up to show you the way?
Just take a step forward and
I promise you that with each
step you take, another light
will shine ... the path
will never be dark.
Today, let's take the
next step together, shall we?

_____

_____

_____

_____

_____

_____

_____

_____

_____

_____

_____

_____

_____

Doodles & Dreams...

...and More!

The Gates are Open!

The gateways to a happier, more magical life are open...
will you walk through?
Come on, hold hands with me and let's walk into your magical life..
What does it look like on the other side of the gateway?

_____
_____
_____
_____
_____
_____
_____
_____
_____
_____
_____
_____
_____
_____
_____
_____
_____
_____
_____
_____

Sit and Listen!

Today, let's find a place to sit
quietly and listen to your
inner voice ... it's giving you
messages filled with love
about how to handle what is
heavy on your mind.
Our gift to ourselves today is
simply sitting quietly and
listening to our hearts ....
What do you hear / feel /
sense?

Let your Light Shine!

How do you show up for your day?
Today, I want you to shine that light
that is in your heart and soul.
Shine it bright for all the world to see.
You have a special light that is
needed on this earth.
Don't hold back, let it shine ...
stand with other bright lights and see
just how bright this earth can be!
Who do you stand with that makes you
shine brighter...

_____

_____

_____

_____

_____

_____

_____

_____

Peace

If we want peace, we must be in peace
with ourselves and others.
I believe our primary purpose for being on this earth,
at this time, is to be a role model for peace.
Let there be peace on earth .... and let it begin with me!
How do you spread peace each and every day?

_____

_____

_____

_____

_____

_____

_____

_____

_____

_____

_____

_____

_____

Make Yourself Blush

Today, let's share with
someone something that
happened either today, or
in your past, that made you
feel like you're a force to be
reckoned with. Wear your
"superman cape" loud
and proud today!
What color is your cape?

_____

_____

_____

_____

_____

_____

Take Baby Steps

No one ever said you needed to take huge strides with each and every step, all day long. Sometimes you may need to take a few baby steps. Today, when you feel stressed out, or in doubt, focus on taking smaller steps and see how it can calm you. What are the steps that you will take today?

_____

_____

_____

_____

_____

_____

_____

_____

_____

_____

_____

_____

_____

Watch Me!

Toss out the "I can't"
... dump the "if only"
and loose the "why
me?" ... then listen.
What do you hear?
It is the sound of
"I can" and "I will" now
go out and shout,
"Watch Me!"
What are we going to
watch you do?

_____

_____

_____

_____

_____

_____

_____

_____

_____

_____

_____

_____

_____

_____

_____

_____

Truth of who you are

Don't be afraid to tell the truth of who you are, and
what you want for your life ... even if it winds up
scaring some folks away.
What truth do you need to tell someone?
If telling the truth of who you are and what you want
for your life, scares people ... then just breathe.
Today, don't hold back who you are and
what you want in this lifetime.
What do you want people to know about you?

_____

_____

_____

_____

_____

_____

_____

Doodles and Dreams...

...and More!

Love is the
Answer

It really doesn't matter what
the question is you are
asking or thinking about,
because the answer to most
questions is: Love!
Love yourself more, show
more love to one another.
It really is that simple ....
Choose love!
When did you choose love
today, and how did it affect
the situation?

_____
_____
_____
_____
_____
_____
_____
_____
_____
_____
_____
_____
_____
_____
_____
_____
_____
_____

Happy

When you think happy
thoughts, you live happy.
So, breathe in happy,
feel happy and then
live a happy life.
It really is that simple.
I dare you to give it a try.

_____

_____

_____

_____

_____

_____

_____

_____

_____

_____

_____

_____

_____

_____

_____

_____

_____

_____

_____

_____

_____

_____

_____

_____

It's Your Journey

Not everyone will
understand your
journey.
But that's okay,
because it's not their
journey to be on ...
it is 100% yours!
Stand in the freedom
of being on your
own journey.
You may create it
however you like ...
how creative can
you be?

_____

_____

_____

_____

_____

_____

_____

_____

_____

_____

_____

_____

_____

Grateful

Sometimes we spend a lot of
time looking and longing for
what we have lost.
When we stop looking at what
we have lost, we can get a better
view of what we have.
Challenge yourself to find a
deeper sense of gratitude for
what you have!
What are you truly grateful for
today?

_____

_____

_____

_____

_____

_____

_____

_____

_____

_____

_____

_____

_____

_____

_____

_____

_____

_____

The Awesome Life!

Whoever said life had to be perfect to be
awesome was not truthful.
Life IS awesome ... just because you have a tough day,
doesn't mean you have a tough life.
It was just one day.
That is the greatest thing about life, we get a
"do-over" tomorrow!

_____

_____

_____

_____

_____

_____

_____

_____

_____

_____

_____

_____

_____

_____

_____

_____

_____

_____

_____

_____

_____

_____

Lucky Day!

Today is your lucky day!
Something wonderful is
going to happen to you
today ... I promise!
As you get up and get
moving, look for
something that you will
see as lucky to come
your way!
May the luck of the Irish
be with you.
What lucky things have
happened to you?

Take care of you!

Self-care is extremely important.
Today, start your day filling up
your cup, take a moment to
meditate, count your blessings,
journal and eat a little breakfast.
When you take care of yourself
first, it is the best gift to
yourself and others!
How will you take care of
yourself today?

_____

_____

_____

_____

_____

_____

_____

_____

_____

_____

Just Sing!

Have you ever just wanted to go to the top of the
mountain and sing a song to the world? Today, let's all
pretend that we are on that mountain top singing songs
of joy, love and peace for this world. Will you join me?
What songs will you sing?

_____

_____

_____

_____

_____

_____

_____

_____

_____

_____

_____

_____

_____

_____

_____

_____

_____

_____

_____

_____

_____

_____

_____

_____

Easy does it!

Easy does it soul sister!
Stop trying so hard to
control everything.
All the doors will open in due
time ... sit back and take
it easy today!
Just take a breath in and
write how it feels when you
take it easy...

_____

_____

_____

_____

_____

_____

_____

_____

_____

_____

_____

_____

_____

_____

_____

Express Yourself!

Today, let's express your individuality. Allow yourself to shine, fully shine, because you are awesome!
What parts of you are you going to fully express today?

_____

_____

_____

_____

_____

_____

_____

_____

_____

_____

_____

_____

_____

_____

_____

_____
_____
_____
_____
_____
_____
_____
_____

Inhale ...
Exhale ...

Inhale love, light
and peace ...
exhale anything
that no longer
serves your
highest good.
Repeat, Repeat,
Repeat!

_____
_____
_____
_____
_____
_____
_____
_____
_____
_____
_____
_____
_____

Supersize

We always seem to spend time
trying to shrink our fears ...
but what if we SUPERSIZE our
courage, strength and
abilities instead?
I say, SUPERSIZE me please!
What are you going to
supersize today?

Doodles & Dreams...

...and More!

Dear

Addiction

Today, let's write
good-bye letters to
the bad habits you are
ready to break!
Then let's start some
new, healthier habits
to replace them!
Which letters do you
need to write?

_____

_____

_____

_____

_____

_____

_____

_____

Shine Bright!

How many lights do you think it would take if you
wrapped them around yourself to match the
bright light of your heart and soul?
Your heart is begging you to let it shine.
Toss on your sunglasses, turn on your lights and
let's light up the world together!
Shine on, my friend!

_____

_____

_____

_____

_____

_____

_____

_____

Rising up!

Nothing can hold a
Phoenix down, it rises
from the ashes and
flies into greatness.
Today, let's free our
inner Phoenix and
rise up!

_____

_____

_____

_____

_____

_____

_____

_____

_____

_____

_____

_____

_____

_____

_____

_____

_____

_____

_____

_____

_____

_____

_____

_____

Flame inside of you!

What is burning inside of you?
We all have passion and energy that is
burning, trying to get to the surface.
Sit quietly today and go deep inside ...
listen to what wants to be heard,
what wants to be expressed and what
wants to surface for you.

Eat Dessert First!

One thing my mom
always taught us was to
eat dessert first!
I always crack up when
wait staff tell my mom
to save room for some
famous dessert.
Mom looks up and says,
"Heck, I'll just eat the
delicious dessert first
and save room for
dinner!"
She's not kidding ...
so let's try it today.
Enjoy your dessert first!

The grass is greener!

Have you ever looked
over a fence and thought
the grass looked
greener?
You have two choices:
take care of the grass on
your side or jump
the fence!
Focus on the grass under
your feet, take care of it.
Make it your goal to
have people look at your
"grass" and wonder how
you got it to look
so good!
What will you do today
to make the grass
greener on your side of
the fence?

_____

_____

_____

_____

_____

_____

_____

Up Stream?

Which direction are you paddling your life?
Are you fighting life and paddling upstream with all
of your might, trying to prove to yourself that
life has to be tough?
Or are you paddling your life downstream,
enjoying the sights along the way?
Life can be simple if you just turn your
boat around and float!

_____

_____

_____

_____

_____

_____

_____
_____
_____
_____
_____
_____
_____
_____
_____
_____
_____
_____
_____
_____
_____
_____
_____
_____
_____
_____
_____

Show us your Avatar!

What does your Avatar look like? Is it a big scary monster? An amazing super hero? A delicate butterfly or maybe something in between. Find an Avatar that feels right for you and post it somewhere you can see it and let your Avatar shine! Draw a picture of your avatar!

Doodles & Dreams...

...and More!

Peek a Boo!

Peek-a-boo, I see you ...
a childhood game and yet
on any day we hide who
we are from the world.
Today, I say jump out
from behind the mask and
the hats that we wear and
let the world see you ...
the masterpiece
that you are!
What are you hiding from
the world?

_____
_____
_____
_____
_____

_____
_____
_____
_____
_____
_____
_____
_____
_____
_____
_____
_____

Laughter!

Today, spend time
with a friend and
laugh ... laugh until
one of you runs to the
bathroom before they
pee their pants, this is
the moment you
know the laughter got
into your heart
and soul.
Laughter cures all!
What are your
favorite movies / TV
shows that make you
laugh, make a list.
Then make a list of
which friends make
your heart and soul
laugh and feel light.

_____
_____
_____

_____

_____

_____

_____

_____

_____

_____

_____

_____

_____

_____

_____

_____

_____

_____

Best Day Ever!

Today is a day to celebrate all
the wishes that you've ever
asked for ... trust they are going
to be granted.
Everything you have ever
wanted is coming true!
Today is the BEST DAY EVER!
List everything that happened
today to make it the best day
ever... start with you are alive!

_____

_____

_____

_____

_____

_____

_____

_____

_____

_____

Healthy Living!

Today, let's focus on maintaining or improving your health. Let's say thanks to your body for supporting you every day. Take a minute and write a "thank you" note to your hands, feet, legs, arms, eyes, heart, lungs etc. for working at their perfect function. Amen!

_____
_____
_____
_____
_____
_____
_____
_____

_____
_____
_____
_____
_____
_____
_____
_____
_____
_____
_____
_____
_____
_____

_____
_____
_____
_____
_____
_____
_____
_____
_____

Take a Walk!

Go for a walk in a beautiful space surrounded by nature …
have a chat with the Angels and Fairies.
You'll be amazed at what truth and empowering
information comes to you.
What did you learn on your walk?

_____
_____
_____
_____
_____
_____
_____
_____

_____
_____
_____
_____
_____
_____
_____
_____
_____
_____
_____

Strength

Today, why not begin
your day with your
shoulders back and
your head held high?
Simply shifting your
posture to one of
strength will bring
this personal quality
from within.
Try it and be ready to
be transformed.

Challenges

Challenges are something the soul loves, for nothing makes us grow faster than stepping out of our comfort zone. Today, welcome the challenges and look at them as an opportunity to grow into something even more amazing! What lessons have your challenges taught you lately?

_____

_____

_____

_____

_____

_____

_____

_____

What is your plan?

Let's make a plan ... look back on what you set as
magical goals for yourself. What's working and what
needs to be adjusted? Today, let's adjust and get
going on our magical plans. You deserve it!
Write your magical plan here...

_____

_____

_____

_____

_____

_____

_____

_____

Doodles & Dreams...

...and More!

Journal

_____
_____
_____
_____
_____
_____
_____
_____
_____
_____
_____
_____
_____
_____
_____
_____
_____
_____
_____
_____
_____
_____
_____
_____
_____
_____

_____
_____
_____
_____
_____
_____
_____
_____
_____
_____
_____
_____
_____
_____
_____
_____
_____
_____
_____
_____
_____
_____
_____
_____
_____
_____

Hello Beautiful Soul...

Hello Beautiful Soul...

Thank you so much for choosing my "In Soul Motion" Journal. This Journal was created completely out of love. It all started from the inspirational messages I was sending to friends every morning ... but the list of friends soon became too large and it was taking me all morning to send.

So the *In Soul Motion* app was created ... you can download it for FREE for a daily dose of happiness!

(Available in the App Store for Apple & Google.)

A few months after the app was available, I started working on the *"In Soul Motion"* card deck and journal ... the card deck will give you a boost of inspiration to create more happiness in your life and in this world. The journal is yet another way to focus inward to create happiness, with more messages and inspiring actions you can take, or do, to connect to your heart and soul for a deeper sense of happiness!

If you'd like to connect up with me, I offer my Angel Readings, in-person, or via Skype.

I'm also an inspirational mentor, speaker & teacher. For my list of offerings, visit my website: **www.cherylcarrigan.com**.

I love to hear from people who have any of my "In Soul Motion" products, so please join me via Facebook or feel free to drop me an email: info@InSoulMotion.com.

Inspiring Soul Connections!

Love,

Cheryl

Made in the USA
Lexington, KY
23 March 2017